THE
COIN COLOURING BOOK

ARRANGED CHRONOLOGICALLY, INCLUDING SOME BRIEF RELEVANT FACTS;

WITH THIRTY-SIX DRAWINGS OF ENGLISH AND BRITISH COINS FROM THE EARLIEST TIMES TO THE PRESENT DAY

COMPILED BY

CHRISTOPHER HENRY PERKINS

FIRST EDITION, WITH DRAWINGS BASED PRINCIPALLY ON THE ORIGINAL WORKS OF F. W. FAIRHOLT & F. J. LEES

COIN PUBLICATIONS, LONDON SE20

MMXVII

FOREWORD

Historically, coins have always been very lacking in colour, being made of a single piece of metal. The things they depict though; the faces, plants, heraldry, swords, ships, crowns, horses etc, are all actually very colourful in real life. I personally believe that coins are the ideal candidate to add colour to. Use this book to create realistic life-like coloured works of art, or go wild with them and colour them in your own fantastic style. Most have been waiting for centuries just for you to add a bit of colour to them!

Note that the paper selected for this book is thick and should be suited to both colouring pencils and standard felt-tipped pens. Some felt-tipped pens may bleed through to the other side if held on the paper for longer periods of time.

BACKGROUND

'The Coin Colouring book' is, as far as I can tell, the first ever colouring book featuring just images of coins. The coin line drawings contained within this book are all British coins (technically English coins and then British coins after the 1707 Act of Union) and they are arranged in chronological order.

Having collected a few old books on coins of the British Isles for personal reference I knew that some of them contained very detailed engravings of coins. It occurred to me that these images in a much larger format, would be perfect for use in a modern colouring book. Two old books form the basis for the line drawings in this book, namely 'The Silver Coins of England' (3rd edition, 1887) originally by Edward Hawkins and updated after his death by his grandson Robert Lloyd Kenyon and 'The Gold Coins of England' (1st edition 1884) also by Robert Lloyd Kenyon.

The original drawings in the books were too small and had to be adapted and completely re-drawn digitally. Nevertheless, sincere gratitude should be purveyed upon Messrs Frederick William Fairholt (1814-66) and Frederic James Lees (1842-97), the artists who painstakingly drew hundreds of highly detailed drawings found in the aforementioned books. The later coin drawings, from page thirty-two onwards have been newly drawn by artistic agencies and are based on modern photographs of the coins concerned. Special thanks to Ankit Kumar for some of the modern coin images and especially the amazingly detailed Victorian Gothic crown (pages 32 and 33).

CHP
Sep. 2017

CONTENTS

King Tasciovanus of the Celtic Catuvellauni Tribe

This is a gold coin known to us modern folk as a 'Stater'. The original coin is about 17mm in diameter (a bit smaller than a current 5p). It was made approximately between the last part of the 1st century BCE to the early part of the 1st century CE (about 2,047 to 2,008 years ago). The territory of King Tasciovanus is thought to have centred on where the modern town of St. Albans is now located. Very little is known about King Tasciovanus. The letters T, A, S and C can be seen around the horseman.

King William I (AKA William the Conqueror), 1066 - 1087

This is a silver penny, about 20mm in diameter (about the same as a modern penny). King William ruled from 1066 to 1087, but only on very early coins was he shown as facing left. 'PILLE-MUS REX' means 'William, King'. On the other side is 'DUNNIC ON AESTI' (the conjoined AE are worn off). Dunnic is the name of the man who struck the coin, 'ON' means 'of' and 'AESTI' is an abbreviation for the town of Hastings. This coin was made in Hastings, shortly after the battle!

King Edward IV, 1461 - 1470 and 2nd reign 1471 - 1483

This is a gold Ryal (sometimes known as a rose-noble), made between 1464 - 1470 with a diameter of about 35mm. The King's long royal titles start at about 2 O'clock with 'ED' and continue after the prow of his ship with 'WARD', then 'DI GRA' and so on, listing his territories of England, France and Ireland. On the rear of the ship is a large standard showing a letter 'E' for Edward.

King Henry VII, 1485 - 1509

This is a very large gold Sovereign with a diameter of about 42mm. The King's long royal titles start at about 2 O'clock with 'HENRICUS DEI GRA' and continue in the usual manner, mentioning his territories of England, France and Ireland. The King is sitting on a wide throne that goes all the way to the top of the coin.

King Edward VI, 1547 - 1553

This is a very large silver Crown with a diameter of about 42mm. The King's long royal titles start after the barrel at the top with 'EDWARD VI D G' and continue in the usual manner, mentioning his territories of England, France and Ireland. A very new idea at the time was to put the date on the coin – '1552' can be seen under the King's horse.

Queen Mary (AKA Bloody Mary), 1553-54

This is a sovereign, struck in gold like modern sovereigns but much larger, with a diameter of about 43mm.

Queen Mary with her husband, Philip of Spain, 1554 - 1558

This is a silver shilling, the actual coin is about 31mm in diameter and is marked on the reverse with 'XII' on either side of the crown to denote 12 pence (a shilling). The obverse shows the date 1554. Some of the letters on the obverse are no longer fully visible – they read 'PHILIP ET MARIA D G' followed by abbreviations of their combined territories.

Elizabeth I, 1558-1603

A silver sixpence coin, dated 1591 with Elizabeth abbreviated to just 'ELIZAB'. These were about 25mm in diameter (about the same size as a modern 2p, but much thinner). Note the irregular shape of the coin? This is caused by people who used to clip or shave off small amounts of silver to save, before attempting to spend the coin as normal.

Elizabeth I, 1558-1603

A crown, made of silver with a diameter of about 42mm. The digit '1' mint-mark (which looks a bit like a 'Z') dates this coin to 1601-2. Before the practice of putting actual dates on coins was widely practiced, often the only way of telling when the coin was made is by identifying its mint-mark. Mint-marks were symbols, shapes or sometimes letters that were changed roughly annually during this period.

James I, 1603-25

A Rose-Ryal, made of gold with a diameter of about 46mm. The trefoil mint-mark (a pattern of three leaves, seen at the top before the king's Latin name 'IACOBUS') dates this coin to 1613.

Charles I, 1625-49

Struck at Oxford during the English civil war, this triple unite denomination (note the Roman numerals 'III' on the reverse) was made of gold and had a diameter of about 46mm.

Charles I, 1625-49

The mint-mark on this coin is coincidentally a crown (the same as the coin's denomination) which indicates that it was struck 1635-1636. The large crown coin was made of silver and had a diameter of about 44mm.

William and Mary, 1689-94

Queen Mary Stuart reigned jointly with her husband William of Orange. She died of smallpox in 1694, aged 32. William ruled without her until his death in 1702. This is a two guinea coin, which was made of gold and had a diameter of about 30mm (a bit bigger than a modern £2 coin).

THE COIN COLOURING BOOK

Queen Anne, 1702-14

Unlike her predecessor (and brother-in-law) King William III, Queen Anne insisted that she be shown on gold coins wearing some clothes, and not with a bare neck and chest! This is a five guinea denomination, which was the highest denomination at the time and would have been a very large amount of money. They were made of gold and had a diameter of about 37mm.

Queen Victoria, 1837 - 1901

The intricate 'Gothic' style 1847 Victorian crown is one of the highest regarded British coin designs of the last couple of centuries. It wasn't actually struck to be used, but was instead made in much smaller numbers and to a very high standard. They were made of sterling silver and had a diameter of 38.6mm (the same as modern UK £5 coins).

King Edward VII, 1901-10

The florin had a face value of, and was sometimes called a 'two shillings'. It was introduced during the reign of Queen Victoria in 1849. The popular standing Britannia design was only featured on the reverse during the short reign of King Edward VII. They were made of sterling silver, 28.5mm in diameter (a little larger than a modern 50p) and could actually be spent as 10p right up to 1992!

King George V, 1910-36

New designs for all coins were revealed in 1927, including this attractive large silver crown, which is usually referred to as a 'wreath crown' due to the wreath that it features, made up of English roses, Scottish thistle and Irish clover. Older crowns like this one are 38.6mm in diameter, which is the same size as modern UK £5 coins.

King George V, 1910-36

The silver shilling was a very important old denomination with a fair bit of buying power. It was replaced by the modern decimal 5p, but at 23.6mm in diameter it was much larger than our current 5p. It was 1/20th of a pound and could actually be spent as 5p right up to 1990!

King George VI, 1936-52

The Golden Hind galleon was featured on the reverse of British half-penny coins from 1937 to 1967 (and again in 1970). The coins were made of bronze and were 26mm in diameter, which is about the same size as a modern 2p.

Queen Elizabeth II, 1952-date

The 2009 Kew Gardens 50p was made to mark the 250th anniversary of Kew Gardens. It shows the Chinese Pagoda which is at the south-east corner of Kew Gardens. All modern 50p coins are 27.3mm in diameter. The original 50p coins replaced the 10 Shilling bank note in 1969.

Queen Elizabeth II, 1952-date

The new 12-sided bi-metallic £1 coin was introduced in 2017 with very large numbers of 2016 and 2017 dated coins entering circulation at about the same time. The coin is 23.03mm from flat to flat, 23.43mm measured point to point and about 3mm thick.

Now that you're a fully qualified chromanumismatist* (a new term to describe someone who studies the intricacies of coins while applying colour to them) you may be interested in some of these reference books published by the same publisher:

Concerning old coins:

Roman Base Metal Coins - A Price Guide: is a book containing many line drawings of the most commonly encountered copper, bronze and brass Roman coins, in date order and with handy tips to aid identification as well as guide values.

Roman Silver Coins - A Price Guide: as above, for Roman silver coins.

England's Striking History: a lot of history and a lot of coins; an excellent introduction to the hammered silver coinage of England covering 959 to about 1660.

Collectors' Coins Great Britain 1760 - 1970: A price-guide book for all British coins, covering 1760 - 1970 and with more detail on coin varieties than any other similar book. With lots of facts and figures (published approximately bi-annually).

Collectors' Coins Ireland (1660 - 2000): A price-guide to all Irish coins covering Charles II to the pre-Euro decimal coinage.

Concerning modern coins:

Collectors' Coins - Decimal Issues of the UK: One of the best-selling books on British coins, and the most detailed coverage of UK decimal coins in change including the various precious metals/collectors editions, all with values given (published annually). See also checkyourchange.co.uk for details of the 'Check Your Change' app.

Other more specialised books on coins and medals are available from Coin Publications and many other reputable publishers.

* From the Greek 'chroma' meaning 'colour' and the word 'numismatist' which came from a French word with its roots in Latin and Greek and means someone who studies coins.